Waterloo News

Monday morning in Waterloo School...

Mrs Jones wants us to make a school newspaper.
It will be called Waterloo News.
You are all going to help me make the newspaper.
The newspaper can go to all the children in the school.
Mr Flint says that we can put the Waterloo News
next to the other newspapers in his shop.
We have to finish the newspaper by Friday!

3

5

After tea, Rocky started to draw…

After tea, Wing Chan started to draw…

Jamila ran into the park.

Fred knows all about how to grow things.
He will help me with my garden report.

Fred was weeding the roses.

What's happening in the garden, Fred?
I have to do a report for the school newspaper.

Fred dug his spade into the soil.

Oh! It's bad news, I'm afraid.
I've got a touch of black spot.
You could do a report on that if you like.

That sounds terrible!
Is it bad?

After tea, Ben thought about his sports report...

The only school sports in the last two weeks was our last school football match.

Well, do a report on that.

After tea, Tony and Tessa went out on their bikes.

Let's go and find some news!

OK.

Yes.
Mrs Nash said we were Good Samaritans.

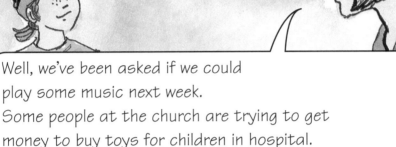

Well, we've been asked if we could
play some music next week.
Some people at the church are trying to get
money to buy toys for children in hospital.
They are putting on a show next week in the church hall.
I said we would lend a hand.

Great! I don't mind lending a hand,
and it could lead to bigger things!

THE MOON
Hit record for Potts Twins!

Hey! I could do a report on that!
People would like to read about
how we sing and play music.

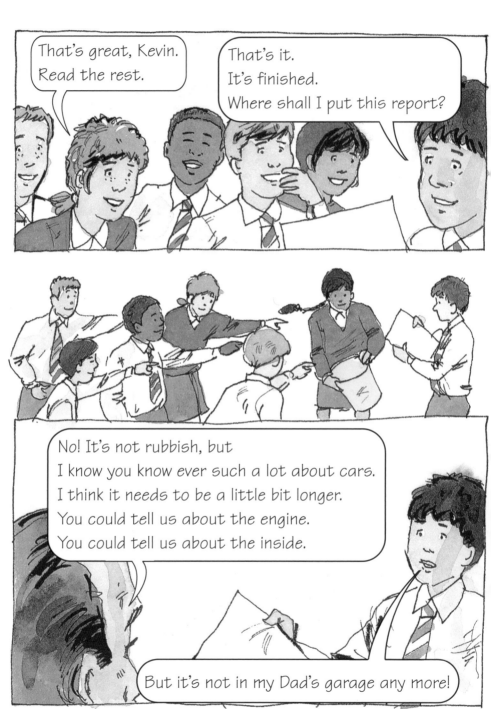

19

Don't worry, Jamila.
Black spot is something that you get on a rose.
People don't get black spot.
Fred was talking about his roses.
You have to pull off the leaves with
black spots and put them on a fire.
Still, that will be a good report.
You must go back to Fred and
find out all about it.
Have you done a sports report, Ben?

It's about our last football game.

Ben read his football report.
It was very long…

The famous Tessa Potts will be singing and
playing the drums in a show next week in the church hall.
This clever girl, who was born in Wellington Square,
started to play music at the age of five.
She is now really well known for her brilliant drum playing.
Other people in the Potts family will also be playing.

Tessa singing in
show next week!

Other people!
Dad will be playing his trumpet.
I will play the guitar and so will Mum.
The music comes from
the two guitars and the trumpet.
All you do is go bang, bang, bang!

That will do, Tony.
But Tony is right, Tessa.
You do need to talk about other people.

27

31